LONDON
MUSEUM

ZILLAH
HALLS

MEN'S COSTUME 1750-1800

LONDON:
HER
MAJESTY'S
STATIONERY
OFFICE
1973

CW01024230

SBN 11 290161 1

Men's Costume 1750-1800

The period 1750-1800 was one of political and cultural upheaval which was reflected, as always, in the fashionable costume of men and women alike. Women were transformed from the richly coloured and tightly restricted creatures of the middle of the century to the pallid nymphs of the years around 1800, their almost natural forms revealed, their movements unfettered: their male counterparts, similarly influenced, underwent comparable changes in their appearance. It was the expression of a romantic enthusiasm for nature as seen through the eyes of art; an enthusiasm that led ladies to wear diaphanous garments which could have afforded little protection from the damp and chill of genuine country surroundings but which none the less suggested the unspoilt child of nature rather than the over elaborate product of urban civilisation.

The new style owed in fact a great deal to art; tailoring had never before been so skilled, and the plain dark cloth of the late-18th century (no 21, Plate 17) was of superb quality. This was the beginning of the age of Beau Brummel; it was also the commencement of the prestige of English tailoring and its supremacy over French male fashion. The English love of country life – so delightfully portrayed in D. Allen's *The Family of Sir James Hunter Blair* – was yet another factor in this trend, the appearance of the English country gentleman according perfectly with Rousseau's popular call for a turning-back to the simple natural life.

The garment that survives from this period in the greatest quantities is the waistcoat, and it is here that the parallel changes in men's and women's costume can be seen most clearly. The general trend from the full skirted, boldly patterned garment of the 1750's and 1760's (no 50, Plate 1) to the short, tubular and delicately patterned waistcoat of the last decade of the century (no 93, Plate 20) is directly comparable with the change from the 1750's dress, made in boldly patterned brocade draped over side-hoops, to the pale and slender dress of the late 1790's, the long pointed line now high and quite straight. The character of the decoration of the waistcoat again changes in a way comparable

3

with the development of women's dress – the delicate patterns of the late 18th-century waistcoat being akin to the small woven or embroidered spots or narrow stripes of contemporary dress fabrics. During the 1780's waistcoats embroidered with pictorial subjects were fashionable, and in Plates 15 and 16 (nos 73 and 77), the charming, still slightly rococo designs, depict once again the popular feeling for country life; while the influence of Neo-classicism, emergent in England since the 1760's, is evident in the applied medallions and embroidered urns of Plate 21 (no 106).

The fashionable man of the 1750's, as depicted in Allan Ramsay's portrait of Francis Child, was clad in silk, often elaborately woven, his full skirted large cuffed coat being frequently padded, and worn over the elongated flamboyantly decorated style of waistcoat. The effect, as may be seen in Plate 2 (no 2), was magnificent rather than practical, evoking the artificial existence of the townsman rather than the active life of the countryman.

Francis Child by Allan Ramsay 1758 (Earl of Jersey)

4

By the latter years of the century the heavy skirts (no 26, Plate 3) had disappeared – the silks and satins giving way to a more practical fine cloth (no 43, Plate 19). And while the elaborate and skilful tailoring, the skin-tight breeches and white linen, could scarcely have been more functional than the earlier style, they none the less created the impression – as in Ibbetson's portrait of the young George Biggin – of a garb more suited to horseback than to the street.

Fine cloth reached the pinnacle of fashion at the end of the century, the King himself appearing at a reception in 1795 in 'a prune-coloured coat of broadcloth'; and the material eventually received its final accolade from that arbiter of fashion, Beau Brummel. Brummel's conception of men's clothes was architectural rather than pictorial, the clear-cut lines of his suits being a subtle means of expressing social

Portrait of an Unknown man by Pompeo Batoni 1778 (Photo, Witt Library)

superiority. 'If John Bull turns to look after you', he once remarked, 'you are not well dressed.'

Breeches changed only slightly, becoming increasingly closer fitting and with a deeper waistband to balance the shortened waistcoat; braces came into general use just before 1790. Although generally 'en suite' with the suit, towards the end of the century breeches were often of a contrasting colour (usually lighter) or fabric; buckskin, once worn only by servants or ruffians, now began to enter the wardrobe of the gentleman. Shirts changed even less. The cravat or stock increased in height so that it had to be supported by stiffening; its arrangement also became increasingly complex at the end of the century.

Of necessity the other accessories of dress altered to suit the changes in fashion. Men's wigs, for instance, closely followed women's hairdressing trends, and their hats had similarly to change to suit the new styles. Indeed the bicorne hats which appeared at the end of the century were carried under the arm rather than worn. Round hats (no 124, Plate 22) were much favoured by those who preferred to wear a hat, while the tricorne, fashionable earlier in the

The Wilkinson Family attributed to Francis Wheatley c 1778 (Detroit Institute of Arts)

century, continued to be worn by servants and the lower classes.

For greater ease the English gentleman would remove his tight-fitting coat and entertain his guests in the studied relaxation of a dressing-gown, 'banyan' or Indian gown. This comfortable garment, described by Dr Johnson in his *dictionary* as 'a loose gown worn before one is formally dressed',

George Biggin by J. C. Ibbetson 1783 (Mr and Mrs Paul Mellon)

had steadily grown in favour from the late-17th century. It was extremely popular in the 1780's, sometimes being worn out of doors, although by this time it was more like a coat. 'Banyans are worn in every part of the town from Wapping to Westminster, and if a sword is occasionally put on it sticks out of the middle of the slit behind. This however is the fashion, the ton, and what can a man do? He must wear a banyan', the *Town and Country Magazine* reported in 1785. Doubtless the fashion owed much to that longstanding English taste for the exotic which brought to London such imports as chintz, lacquer, porcelain and tea. Indeed the dressing-gown (no 132, Plate 11) is itself made of chintz, and the fitted style is closer in cut to its eastern original than to the loose, easy kimono style worn by the Stuart diarist, Samuel Pepys, in the well known portrait by John Hayls.

The Family of Sir James Hunter Blair, 1st Baronet by David Allan 1785 (Sir James Hunter Blair)

Trade card of William Pape, breeches-maker, c. 1758.
On the reverse is a receipt for 'on pound on shilling for a pair of
Buck Skin Breeches for your postlien', 28 June 1758 (London
Museum)

William Pape

At y Breeches & Glove, the
Corner of Gray's Inn-Passage
near Red Lion Square Holborn
Makes and Sells all Sorts of
Leather Breeches at
Reasonable Rates
NB. all Sorts of Riding Gloves.

Plate 1

Waistcoat,
1755-65 (no 50)

Plate 2

Suit,
1760-65 (no 2)

Plate 3   **Coat,**
1760-70 (no 26)

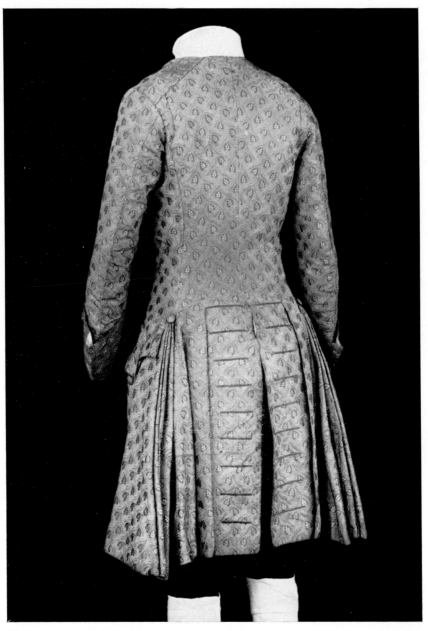

Plate 4   **Suit,**
1765-75 (no 6)

Plate 5   **Waistcoat,**
                     1760-70 (no 52)

Plate 6   **Waistcoat,**
             1765-75 (no 57)

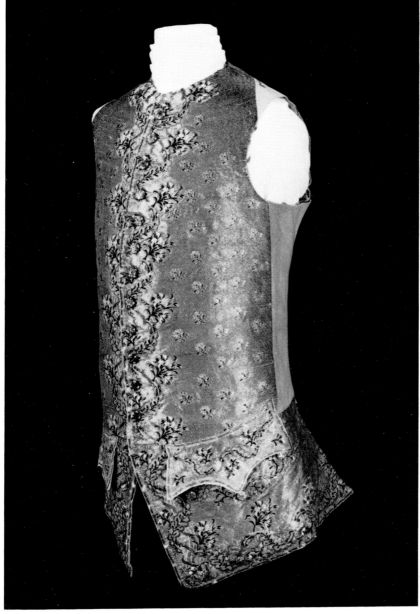

Plate 7   **Waistcoat,**
1770-75 (no 59)

Plate 8   **Waistcoat,**
1770-80 (no 69)

Plate 10   **Detail of
embroidered
coat tails**
(no 11)

Plate 11   **Dressing-gown,**
1770-80 (no 132)

Plate 12

**Detail of waist-
coat**
(no 132)

Plate 13   Waistcoat,
                  1770-80 (no 66)

Plate 14

Waistcoat,
1770-80 (no 70)

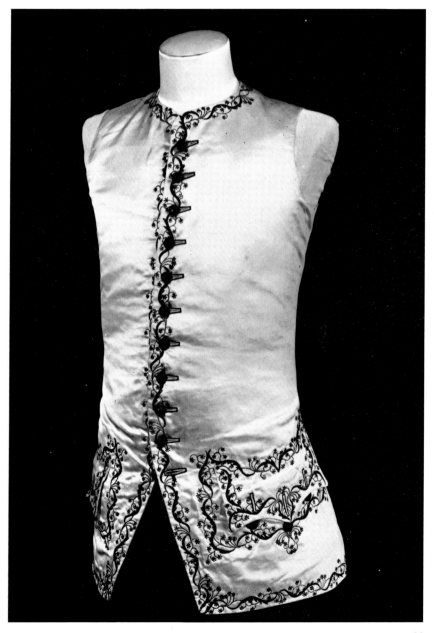

Plate 15(a)

Waistcoat,
1775–85 (no 73)

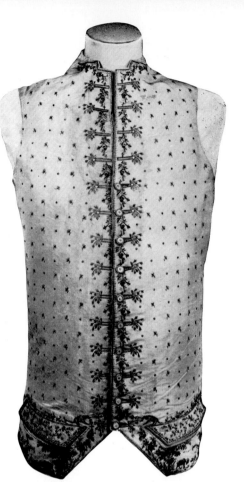

Plate 15(b)

Detail of Waist-coat
(no 73)

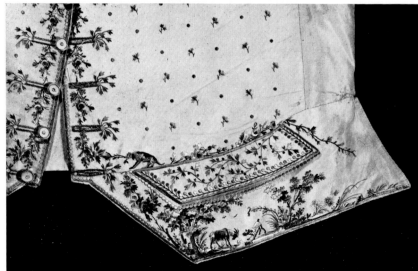

Plate 16   Waistcoat,
          1775-85 (no 77)

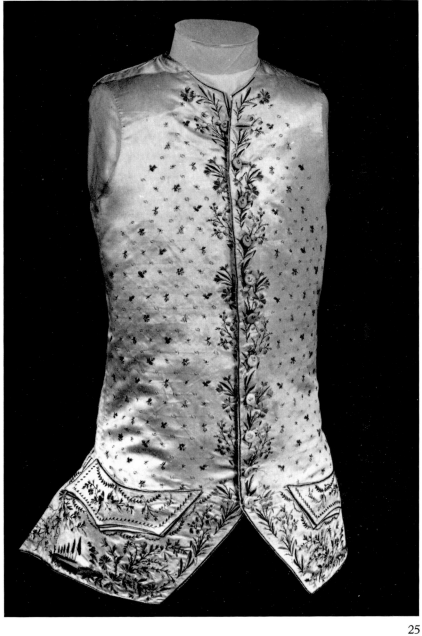

Plate 17   **Suit,**
1780-90 (no 21)

Plate 18   **Waistcoat,**
1780-90 (no 84)

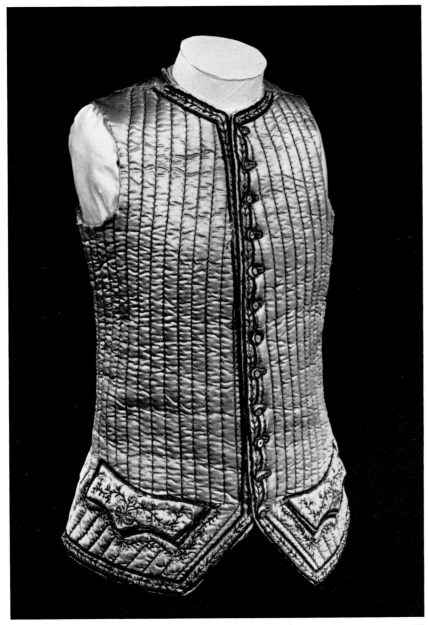

Plate 19

Coat,
1785-95 (no 43)

Plate 20   **Waistcoat,**
1785-95 (no 93)

Plate 21   **Waistcoat fronts,**
(not made up)
1790-1800
(no 106)

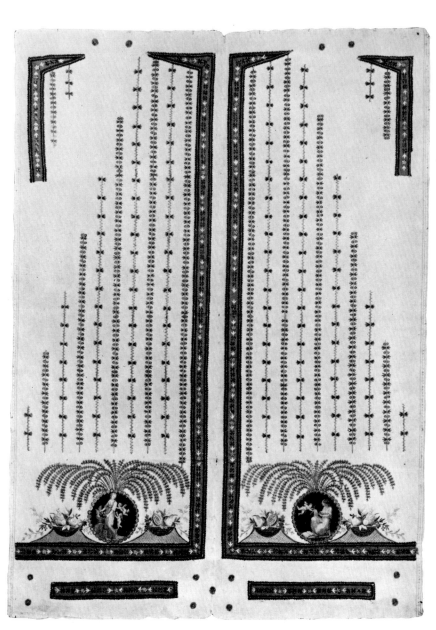

Plate 22   **Hat,**
1790-1800
(no 124)

Catalogue of Men's Costume
1750-1800

Suits

1 **Suit** (coat, waistcoat and breeches), 1750-60; reddish-pink cut and uncut velvet, woven with a little black and white in a trellis pattern with flowers. The coat, and the waistcoat front edges and skirts, are lined with white satin; the rest of the waistcoat and the breeches are lined with a linen and cotton mixture. The coat still shows the wide side-pleats and the large cuffs of the middle years of the century.
Condition: fragile and badly faded
33.113 (LM Cat 1935, p 135)

2 **Suit** (coat, waistcoat and breeches), 1760-65; white silk woven with diagonal silver lines, and with flowers in pink, blue and green uncut velvet. The back of the waistcoat is white linen.
Condition: fairly good except for relining of the coat and waistcoat and alterations to the top of the breeches
A 13037 (formerly 33.114) *Plate 2*

3 **Suit** (coat, waistcoat and breeches), 1760-70; cream velvet printed with a small stem and flower pattern, mostly in green and blue; the coat, and the waistcoat front edges and skirt, are lined with pale blue satin. The rest of the waistcoat lining is a twilled linen and cotton mixture and the back is grey woollen cloth; the breeches also are lined with a linen and cotton mixture.
Condition: good
A 7557 (formerly 33.115)

4 **Suit** (coat and sleeved waistcoat), 1760-70; green and white figured silk woven with a fairly small flower pattern. The coat front edges and the waistcoat front edges and skirt are lined with white twilled silk; the rest of the waistcoat is lined with a mixture of linen and cotton. The coat still has the wide stiffened side-pleats and large cuffs of the middle of the century, but the fabric can be dated 1760-70. The waistcoat has ruched trimming on the pocket flaps and skirt.
Condition: good except that the coat has been relined
A 12985 (LM Cat 1935, p 135)

5 **Suit** (coat and sleeved waistcoat), 1760-70; crimson velvet with fine double lines of uncut velvet; both garments are embroidered with a pattern of flowers and meandering lines in white and yellow, and lined with cream ribbed silk.
Condition: fair; lining very tattered
A 13000 (LM Cat 1935, p 136)

6 **Suit** (coat and waistcoat), 1765-75; fawn cloth, decorated with silver thread and spangle embroidery imitating frogging; the coat is lined with bright pink twilled silk, and the waistcoat front edges and skirt with similar silk; the rest of the waistcoat lining is a cotton and linen mixture.
Condition: good
A 7559 *Plate 4*

7 **Suit** (coat and waistcoat), c 1769; crimson velvet. The coat is lined with cream twilled silk and the waistcoat front edges and skirt are similarly lined. The back of the waistcoat is crimson twilled wool, and the remaining waistcoat lining a mixture of cotton and linen.
The suit is said originally to have belonged to Oliver Goldsmith, possibly that referred to by Boswell in his *Life of Johnson* in the reference to October 16th, 1769.
Condition: good
A 7563 (LM Cat 1935, p 137 ill. Pl. XLVII)

8 **Suit** (coat, waistcoat and breeches), 1770-80; fawn figured velvet, woven in a lozenge pattern with a small floral sprig. The waistcoat front edges are lined with cream twilled silk, the back and the rest of the lining are white linen, and the breeches are lined with white linen. The coat and waistcoat buttons are blue mirror-glass edged with gilt metal.
Condition: fair; later cuffs have been added to the coat which is also relined
A 12999 (LM Cat 1935, p 136)

9 **Suit** (coat and breeches), 1770-80; fawn cloth; the coat, with a narrow turndown collar, is lined with white twilled silk and trimmed with frogging.
Condition: good
A 15033 (LM Cat 1935, p 138)

10 **Suit** (coat, waistcoat and breeches), 1770-80; yellow-green woollen cloth, the coat, and the waistcoat front edges, lined with pink satin, the rest of the waistcoat lined with a linen and cotton mixture. There is no embroidery but the buttons for the coat, and for the knee opening of the breeches, are very decorative, covered with pink and silver foil and spangles.
Condition: good except for the satin lining, perished
A 17425 (LM Cat 1935, p 138)

11 **Suit** (coat, waistcoat and breeches), 1770-80; the coat
and breeches are of gold satin, the cuffs of the coat of
white satin matching the waistcoat, also of white satin.
The coat, waistcoat and kneebands are embroidered
with flowers and peacock feathers in coloured silks. The
coat is lined with white satin, also the waistcoat fronts
and skirt; the back and the rest of the waistcoat lining
is a mixture of cotton and linen.
Condition: good; the coat lining repaired in the
Museum
29.84/1 (LM Cat 1935, p 137)   *Plates 9, 10*

12 **Suit** (coat, waistcoat and breeches), 1770-80; all three
garments are made of green and blue shot silk, embroidered at the edges with a floral pattern in white,
pale pink and green silks worked mostly in satin stitch,
the patterns rather meagre and stylised compared with
the magnificent embroidered patterns of the early and
middle years of the century. The coat and waistcoat
are both lined with white linen.
Condition: good
29.84/2 (LM Cat 1935, p 138)

13 **Suit** (coat, sleeved waistcoat and breeches), 1770-80;
rose-pink satin, the coat lined with the same satin except
the centre back to the waist, which is lined with a
mixture of cotton and linen. The waistcoat sleeves,
back and lining except for the front edges and skirt, are
also cotton and linen, as is the lining of the breeches.
There is no decoration.
Condition: fair; stained
A 15039 (formerly 33.116)

14 **Suit** (coat and waistcoat), 1770-80; pale green uncut
velvet woven with a spot pattern in pink, gold and
darker green. The waistcoat back is of white cotton;
there is no trimming or decoration.
Condition: fair; coat and waistcoat relined
39.20/5

15 **Suit** (coat and breeches), 1775-85; green and black
silk woven with a narrow stripe and spot pattern. The
coat is elaborately embroidered with a floral pattern in
coloured silks and silver thread, and glass spangles at
the edges; the front is lined with cream silk and the
back with white linen, the breeches have a later lining
of black satin.
Condition: very poor
Z 8007

16 **Suit** (coat and breeches), *c* 1780; made of pale blue twilled furnishing silk woven mostly in green, yellow and white with a very large pattern of tall vases, festoons of flowers and curtains opening to reveal a landscape with pheasants. The silk is by Philippe de la Salle; the coat is lined mostly with pink silk, and the breeches with white linen.
Condition: fair
A 13035 (LM Cat 1935, p 138)

17 **Suit** (coat, waistcoat and breeches), 1780-85; white silk woven with narrow gold stripes, and meandering narrow pink and green stripes suggesting a small floral sprig. The coat is lined with white satin, and the waistcoat front edges and skirts are similarly lined but the rest of the waistcoat is lined with white linen; the waistcoat back is of cream cloth. The breeches are lined with linen.
Condition: fairly good; coat and back lining fragile, breeches altered at the waist
A 7561

18 **Suit** (coat, waistcoat and breeches), 1780-85; pale green silk, elaborately embroidered with a flower and leaf pattern mainly in cream, with some pink, blue and green, mostly in stem and satin stitch; the coat and waistcoat are lined with white silk, the breeches with linen.
Condition: good except for the lining of the coat and waistcoat, very fragile and partly replaced, and the back of the waistcoat, completely replaced. The two button-holes for fastening the coat front may be later work
A 13001 (LM Cat 1935, p 138)

19 **Suit** (coat and waistcoat), 1780-85; the coat is of brown striped silk, the waistcoat of white corded silk; both are embroidered with a floral pattern in various coloured silks worked mainly in satin stitch, growing from a meandering stem of spangles which encloses a border of red ribbed silk covered by machine-made net (point net). The presence of this particular net trimming dates the suit after *c* 1778, when the net was first patented. The coat is lined with cream satin, and the waistcoat has a later cotton back and lining.
Condition: worn and slightly soiled; it was worn by Sir Henry Irving as Dorincourt in 'The Belle's Stratagem', 1876. (LM Cat *Stage Costume and Accessories*, 1968, p 33)
38.19/5

20 **Suit** (coat and waistcoat), 1780-90; purple cloth, the coat and the waistcoat fronts lined with cream twilled silk; the coat back is lined with linen. There is no decoration except for the cream silk piping at the edges, and the high quality cut steel buttons.
Condition: fairly good; lining fragile
29.84/3 (LM Cat 1935, p 139)

21 **Suit** (coat, waistcoat and breeches), 1780-90; purple cloth, the coat (except the back to the waist) and the waistcoat front edges and skirts, lined with white satin; the coat back is lined with glazed wool (callamanca) and the rest of the waistcoat with white cotton; the waist-coat back is made of purple glazed wool. The suit is plain except for the decorative white satin piping at the edges and the high quality of the cut steel buttons.
Condition: good
35.44/1   *Plate 17*

22 **Suit** (coat and breeches), 1785-95; mauve-blue silk with narrow stripes of a lighter blue; small flower and leaf pattern embroidered in coloured silks, and red and white lines at all edges; the coat is lined with cream satin.
Condition: good
61.188/1

23 **Suit** (coat and breeches), 1785-95 (possibly Court wear); black velvet without decoration except for the buttons, covered with gold and silver coiled thread. The coat is lined with cream twilled silk.
Condition: fragile and crushed
49.77/11, 12

Coats

24 **Coat,** 1750-60; greenish-grey watered silk, lined with cream silk; the coat is made in the collarless, large-cuffed, full-skirted style of the middle years of the century, without the exaggerated stiffening of the side-pleats characteristic of the years 1730-50.
Condition: good
53.101/11

25 **Coat,** 1755-60; pink and white twilled silk woven with diagonal spindle-shapes, and lined with white silk; the coat is collarless, the cuffs are still large and the side-pleats, though less voluminous than 1730-40, have only just started to move round to the back.
Condition: fragile; the lining is probably a later replacement
39.181/1

26 **Coat,** 1760-70; pinkish-red, pale blue and straw-coloured silk woven in a trellis and leaf pattern, lined with cream twilled silk. The stiffened side-pleats and large cuffs of the middle of the century are still visible though far less pronounced than they had been in 1730-50. The earliest comparable fabric design is dated 1755 (5990.16, by Anna Maria Garthwaite, at the Victoria and Albert Museum), but this pattern is more stylised and is probably later.
Condition: good but faded
A 12982 (LM Cat 1935, p 136)   *Plate 3*

27 **Coat,** 1765-70; blue checkered silk woven with a serpentine floral pattern in rust-colour and white; the front is lined with white satin, the back skirt with white silk, the back to the waist, and the sleeves, with linen; the cuffs are still large, and the side-pleats still fairly wide though without stiffening.
Condition: poor; faded, worn and crushed, the lining very poor
A 12988 (LM Cat 1935, p 135)

28 **Coat,** 1765-75; reddish-pink silk, woven with narrow horizontal stripes and a small white spot pattern; lined with pink silk except the sleeves, lined with white linen; there is a shaped standing collar, and the centre front fastens from the neck to below the waist with eight large buttons of reddish-pink silk woven with silver strip.
Condition: faded and rather fragile
A 15042 (LM Cat 1935, p 136)

29 **Coat,** 1765-75; velvet woven with fine stripes of three shades of green, lined with white satin except for the sleeves, lined with a cotton and linen mixture.
Condition: fair
34.191

30 **Coat,** 1770-75; orange-red velvet, elaborately embroidered with silver strip and coiled thread, lined with white satin, twilled silk and white linen.
Condition: poor and very soiled
A 13003 (formerly 33.117) (LM Cat 1935, p 137)

31 **Coat,** 1770-80; pinkish-fawn poplin (corded silk and wool), lined with cream twilled silk except for the sleeves, lined with linen. The coat is plain, except for the centre front fastening with very decoratively cut mother-of-pearl buttons, with imitation emeralds.
Condition: poor; some buttons missing, some broken
A 12979

32 Coat, 1770-80; mauve satin, embroidered at the edges with a pattern of flowers and grass in various-coloured silks; lined with white satin except for the sleeves, lined with white linen. The style of the coat is very similar to that of the satin suit (no 11).
Condition: faded and fragile; texture impaired by dry cleaning
A 13002 (LM Cat 1935, p 137)

33 Coat, 1775-85; purple velvet woven with a small checker pattern, and elaborately embroidered with wide borders of rose pattern in various-coloured silks; lined with white satin except for the centre back to the waist, and the sleeves, lined with white cotton. The flamboyant nature of the decoration is further enhanced by the use of very decorative cut steel buttons.
Condition: fair; rather faded
A 12998 (LM Cat 1935, p 139, Pls. XIII and XIV)

34 Coat, 1775-85; finely-striped brown and blue silk, the white twilled silk lining forming decorative piping at the edges.
Condition: good
29.84/6

35 Coat, 1775-85; fawn ribbed silk lined with white linen and a little white twilled silk.
Condition: fragile
39.5/76

36 Coat, 1780-85; black checkered velvet, elaborately and extensively embroidered with coloured silks, silk appliqué and spangles in a floral pattern; lined with white satin except for the centre back down to the waist, and the sleeves, lined with linen; fastening down to the waist with embroidered buttons and buttonholes.
Condition: fragile
A 13036 (LM Cat 1935, p 138)

37 Coat, 1780-85; pale green and grey silk woven in a streaky pattern, lined with white twilled silk except the centre back down to the waist, and the sleeves, lined with white linen; the high shaped turned-down collar is sewn down. The centre front fastens with hooks and eyes under large brass buttons with a checker pattern; the large cuffs of the middle of the century have now shrunk to a mere wristband.
Condition: rather fragile; texture impaired by dry cleaning
A 15037

38   **Coat,** 1780-85; black velvet woven with narrow
meandering silver stripes and rings, the rings all sewn
with silver spangles, and the edges elaborately embroidered with applied silver braid, white satin
embroidered with coloured silks and spangles, and
machine net (point net). The presence of this machine-
made net indicates a date after *c* 1778. The front is lined
with cream satin, the back with a linen and cotton
mixture.
Condition: fragile; the lining very torn
47.53/13

39   **Coat,** 1780-90; brown velvet woven with a white spot,
lined with cream twilled cotton, decorative cut steel
buttons. The cut-away shape of the skirt becomes more
exaggerated during the course of the 1780s.
Condition: rather worn
A 12980 (LM Cat 1935, p 139)

40   **Coat,** 1780-90; blue cloth lined with cream
silk except the sleeves, lined with linen; centre front
fastening with eight cut steel buttons.
Condition: very poor, damaged by moth
A 15032

41   **Coat,** 1780-90; black cloth lined with black twilled
silk; without any decoration or decorative features, and
with the standing collar and cut-away front skirts of
the 1780s.
Condition: fairly good
39.5/52

42   **Coat,** 1780-90; brown cloth, centre front fastening with
brass buttons; high turn-down collar, no decoration;
lined with brown twilled silk except for the sleeves,
lined with linen.
Condition: poor; much of the lining missing
41.8/9

43   **Coat,** 1785-95; light blue cloth, unlined except for the
skirts, lined with a slightly darker (? or unfaded) blue
cloth. The coat is still single-breasted and without
revers, but the high turn-down collar is much more
elaborately tailored than earlier garments had been.
Condition: fair; rather soiled and slightly moth-eaten
53.101/17   *Plate 19*

Waistcoats

During the second half of the century, as in the first, the waistcoat was the most decorative item of fashionable male wear; even when it was part of an embroidered suit it was frequently made of a paler colour, with embroidery matching that of the coat (nos 11, 9); thus harmony was retained while attention was focussed on the most fashionable part. Embroidery is the decoration most frequently found, worked on the fabric before the garment was made up. Woven patterns are still worn, with the borders specially woven to fit the shape of the waistcoat fronts; painted or printed patterns are also occasionally found towards the end of the century.

In the second half of the century, the waistcoat became shorter; this corresponded with the gradual rise in the waistline of women's dresses. The completely straight high waistline to be seen in waistcoats from the mid 1780s is a direct parallel with the high straight waistline of women's dresses that was to appear 1795-1800.

44 **Waistcoat,** sleeved, mid-18th century; plain indigo corded silk, the skirts and front edges lined with a thin indigo silk with a small woven spot, the rest of the waistcoat lined with white twilled cotton and linen. The skirts are still fairly long and full and the decorative buttons are of silver strip and gold thread.
Condition: fair; many buttons missing and buttonholes unpicked
50.6/4

45 **Waistcoat,** mid-18th century; the fronts of green silk woven with a pattern of berries and spots, the back skirt of similar material, the back down to the waist of dull green wool; the front edges and skirts are lined with dull green glazed twilled wool, the rest is lined with linen.
Condition: fair; slightly soiled, enlarged at the centre back
Z 744

46 **Waistcoat,** mid-18th century; black corded silk embroidered with a flower pattern in black silk worked in satin stitch; the front edges are lined with black glazed twilled wool, the skirts with black woollen satin, the rest with linen.
Condition: poor
Z 745

47 **Waistcoat,** 1750-60; cream corded silk, the fronts embroidered in black silk worked in satin stitch, in a floral pattern; lined with cream glazed cotton.
Condition: poor; soiled, the black silk rotting
Z 746

48 **Waistcoat**, 1755-65; orange-pink uncut velvet with a
trellis pattern of meandering lines formed of plain silk;
lined with linen. The waistcoat is completely open
down the back, which fastens adjustably with tape ties.
The armholes are bound with black tape, apparently an
18th-century repair.
Condition: poor; soiled and faded, the buttons probably
not original
Z 741

49 **Waistcoat**, sleeved, 1755-65; the fronts, sleeve-ends
and back skirt of pinkish-fawn velvet, figured with small
sprigs on a background of diagonal lines, with borders
of figured silver ribbon; the sleeves and the back to the
waist are of similar coloured corded silk; the front edges
and skirt are lined with white twilled silk, the rest is
lined with white linen and cotton mixture. The armhole
seams are open at the underarm, and the waistcoat is
still long.
Condition: very poor
A 12528

50 **Waistcoat**, 1755-65; crimson uncut velvet, patterned
in cut pile with borders marking the waistcoat front and
skirt edges, and pockets; diagonal spindle-shapes over
the rest of the area; back of striped crimson silk except
for the side-back skirts of plain uncut crimson velvet;
the front edges and the skirt (except the centre back)
are lined with cream glazed twilled wool, the rest with
linen and a cotton and linen mixture.
Condition: fairly good
58.93   *Plate 1*

51 **Waistcoat**, 1760-70; silver tissue woven with meandering trails of roses and brocaded with borders of pink
flowers; the back to the waist is of white linen, the back
skirt and the skirt and centre front lining, are of white
twilled silk, the rest of the lining a linen and cotton
mixture.
Condition: good
Z 8004

52 **Waistcoat**, 1760-70; crimson satin, borders embroidered with stem and flower pattern in silver thread;
the front edges and the skirts are lined with cream
twilled silk, the rest with a cotton and linen mixture.
Condition: fairly good, slightly soiled
A 15029   *Plate 5*

53 **Waistcoat**, 1760-70; cream ribbed cotton with white
ribbed cotton frogging; back white cotton, the fronts
lined with white linen.
Condition: fragile and soiled
34.248

54　**Waistcoat,** sleeved, 1760-70; blue glazed twilled wool; the front edges and skirts are lined with blue twilled wool, the rest with cream linen. Sleeved waistcoats were no longer fashionable though they are occasionally found.
Condition: fair; some moth damage
36.58/1

55　**Waistcoat,** 1760-70; fawn cloth, frogging embroidered in metal thread at centre front fastening with metal thread buttons and button-holes, also on pocket flaps; the front edges and skirts are lined with cream twilled silk, the rest with a linen and cotton mixture.
Condition: fair; silk lining very worn
49.77/6

56　**Waistcoat,** sleeved, 1765-75; red cloth, the front edges and the skirts lined with red glazed twilled wool, the rest lined with a cotton and linen mixture except for the sleeves, lined with linen. There are underarm sections of a single layer of linen; cf. no 49, which has this section of the seam completely open.
Condition: poor; buttons missing
50.6/3

57　**Waistcoat,** 1765-75; gold tissue brocaded with flowers in shades of red and green, the borders and pockets woven with a serpentine leaf pattern and carnations in silver thread and in red, yellow and blue silk including crimped and chenille thread; the borders are further emphasised by embroidery in silver spangles and coiled thread; the back is of golden-yellow cloth, the front and skirt lining are white satin, the rest of the lining a linen and cotton mixture.
Condition: fairly good, the metal rather tarnished
C 2306 　　　　　　　　　　　　　　　　　　*Plate* 6

58　**Waistcoat,** 1765-75; gold tissue brocaded with flowers in green silk and chenille thread, with woven borders, pocket flaps and surrounds embroidered in silver thread, spangles and foil; the back is of apricot-coloured silk; the fronts are lined with cream twilled silk, the back with a linen and cotton mixture.
Condition: poor
A 12533

59　**Waistcoat,** sleeved, 1770-75; pale grey-blue silk brocaded in various colours with cottages, floral sprays and bunches of ribbon. The fabric is comparable with two designs, both French, in Messrs. Warners' collection, dated 1770 and 1771. The waistcoat is unusual in being made of this expensive material throughout; it is usual for the back and the sleeves (except for the ends) to be made of cheaper fabric. The design has been so

carefully matched at the back that the waistcoat must have been made to be seen without a coat. It is lined throughout with cream glazed twilled wool.
Condition: fairly good except for moth damage to the lining
A 7570 (LM Cat 1935, p 135)   *Plate 7*

60 **Waistcoat,** 1770-80; white satin; pockets and borders embroidered with flowers and ribbons, the rest of the fronts with flowers and butterflies, worked in coloured silks mostly in satin stitch; the front and front bottom edges are lined with white satin, the rest of the fronts with a linen and cotton mixture which is also used for the back.
Condition: rather fragile
Z 740

61 **Waistcoat,** 1770-80; gold tissue woven with a pattern of berries and brocaded with rose sprays in shades of pink and green.
Condition: poor; the back has been renewed for later wearing and the whole waistcoat has been relined
A 12534

62 **Waistcoat,** 1770-80; gold and silver fabric woven with a trellis pattern enclosing flowers brocaded in various-coloured silks; the back, and the front lining, are of white linen.
Condition: good
A 12536

63 **Waistcoat,** 1770-80; gold tissue woven with a flower pattern in pink silk and chenille thread; back of yellow silk lined with cream silk.
The waistcoat was made in two separate pieces (now sewn together) to be connected by lacing down the centre back.
Condition: faded, otherwise good
A 12537

64 **Waistcoat,** 1770-80; cream corded silk woven with silver thread, brocaded with wavy lines in crimped yellow and silver thread, and with floral sprays in shades of pink; the back is of cream twilled silk, and the front edges and skirts are lined with similar silk; the rest is lined with a cotton and linen mixture. The material was probably woven no later than 1775.
Condition: fairly good
A 13004

65 Waistcoat, 1770-80; cream silk with a woven spot; the borders and pocket-flaps are embroidered with a stem pattern in silver thread and spangles; the back to the waist is of cream glazed twilled wool, the skirts are of the same material as the front; the front edges and skirts are lined with cream twilled silk, the rest with a linen and cotton mixture.
Condition: good
A 15030

66 Waistcoat, 1770-80; cream satin, meandering ribbon and flower borders, pocket-flaps woven in metal thread, pink and green silk and chenille and emphasised by spangle, foil and metal thread embroidery; all-over sprig woven in silver thread and green silk; back of cream wool; the front and skirts are lined with cream satin, the rest with a linen and cotton mixture.
Condition: good except for the worn satin lining
36.58/2   *Plate 13*

67 Waistcoat, 1770-80; gold tissue, border pattern and all-over sprigs brocaded in pink and green thread and chenille; woven borders, pocket-flaps and surrounds emphasised with embroidery in silver thread, foil and spangles; the back is of apricot-pink cloth; the front edges and skirts are lined with white satin, the rest with a cotton and linen mixture.
Condition: good
36.58/3

68 Waistcoat, 1770-80; silver tissue, the borders, pocket-flaps and surrounds embroidered in flower and festoon pattern in silver thread, spangles and foil; the back is of cream twilled silk, the front edges and skirts lined with similar silk, the rest with a linen and cotton mixture.
Condition: good
46.45/1

69 Waistcoat, 1770-80; cream ribbed silk, borders and pocket-flaps embroidered with stem and flower pattern worked in chain stitch; the front edges and skirts are lined with cream twilled silk, the rest of the lining and back are of a cotton and linen mixture.
Condition: fair, rather soiled
47.53/8   *Plate 8*

70 **Waistcoat,** 1770-80; cream satin, stem and scroll border, pocket-flaps and surrounds embroidered in black silk and silver thread in stem and satin stitch, with french knots and spangles; the back, open down the centre, fastening and adjustable with lacing, is of cream twilled silk; the front edges and skirts are lined with cream twilled silk, the rest with white linen.
Condition: good
49.77/10   *Plate 14*

71 **Waistcoat,** 1770-80; pale blue corded silk; leaf and stem borders, pocket flaps and surrounds, and all-over sprigs, embroidered in silver thread worked in chain stitch and spangles; the back is of blue glazed twilled wool; the front edges and skirts are lined with cream twilled silk, the rest with a cotton and linen mixture. The skirts appear to have been shortened during the course of the 1770s to keep pace with current fashion.
Condition: fragile and soiled
54.78/3

72 **Waistcoat,** 1775-80; cream satin, with standing collar; the borders, skirts and pocket-flaps are richly embroidered with a floral pattern in gold spangles and gold thread, and there are gold spangles over the rest of the area; the front edges and front skirt are lined with cream twilled silk; the rest of the front lining, and the back, are of linen.
The standing collar is a feature that was to become usual after *c* 1780; the front skirts on the other hand still have the length fashionable in the 1760s.
Condition: fair; satin rather worn, but the metal embroidery still bright
A 15054

73 **Waistcoat,** 1775-85; cream corded silk with flower border, floral all-over sprig, trees, dogs and goats on the short skirts embroidered in coloured silks in stem and satin stitch; narrow side insertions of cream twilled silk; back white cotton; the front edges and skirts are lined with cream twilled silk, the rest is lined with white cotton.
Condition: good
A 7572   *Plates 15a, b*

74 **Waistcoat,** 1775-85; crimson satin, borders and pocket-flaps embroidered with a small flower and stem pattern in silver thread and silver strip; back of cream linen; the fronts are lined with linen except for the front edges and skirts, which are lined with crimson satin. The waistcoat is now considerably shorter than the earlier long-skirted type; by the end of the 18th century the skirt was to disappear altogether.
Condition: good
A 13009

75 **Waistcoat,** 1775-85; cream silk, borders and pocket-flaps embroidered with ribbons and flowers in chenille thread, silver thread and spangles; back of cream glazed twilled wool; the front edges and the skirts are lined with cream twilled silk, the rest with a linen and cotton mixture. The short length became fashionable in the years around 1780; but the skirt, though almost vestigial, has not yet disappeared.
Condition: good
33.42

76 **Waistcoat,** 1775-85; cream corded silk; borders, pocket-flaps and all-over sprig, embroidered mostly in brown, pink and yellow silks; the back is of white cotton, the lining of cream woollen satin.
Condition: fair; the back and lining are possibly later replacements
57.78

77 **Waistcoat,** 1775-85; cream satin; flower border, all-over sprigs and flowers and wooded lake on skirts embroidered in coloured silks in stem stitch and satin stitch, and french knots for mossy bank of lake; back of cotton and linen mixture; the fronts lined with white satin.
Condition: good
63.136/1   *Plate 16*

78 **Waistcoat,** 1780-85; cream satin, small stem and flower pattern on borders and pocket-flaps, and all-over sprigs, embroidered in spangles and silver thread; lined with white satin; woollen interlining.
Condition: fair
A 15053

79 **Waistcoat,** 1780-85; cream satin embroidered with all-over sprig in brown chenille, and with flowers and festoons in silks and chenille at the base of the pockets; pockets and borders embroidered with applied cream gauze with small flowers embroidered in chenille over it. The back is of cream glazed wool, the front and skirt lining are of cream twilled silk, the rest of the lining is white linen and cotton mixture.
Condition: good
35.44/3

80 **Waistcoat,** 1780-85; fawn twilled silk, cream figured ribbon borders and edges of slit pockets; the back is of fawn glazed wool; the front edges and the short front skirts are lined with twilled silk matching the waistcoat front, the rest is lined with a linen and cotton mixture.
Condition: good
54.78/4

81 **Waistcoat,** 1780-90; gold and white silk woven in fine
horizontal stripes; the front edges and short skirts lined
with cream twilled silk, the back and the rest of the
lining cream linen.
Condition: poor
Z 8001

82 **Waistcoat,** 1780-90; cream satin, embroidered in
brown chenille with diagonal lines and small floral
borders at the edges and on the slit pockets; the back
is of cream glazed twilled wool; the front and bottom
edges are lined with cream satin, the rest with a cotton
and linen mixture. The waistcoat appears to have under-
gone a change of plan during the course of making; it
was evidently originally designed to have the pockets
with flaps that had been usual up to the early 1780s,
also to have been much longer; it is now fairly short,
with a straight bottom edge with a sewn-on border. It
may originally have been intended to be collarless; the
present collar is a slightly different shade from the rest,
and shows signs of having been marked for an embroidered pattern which does not suit its present
position.
Condition: poor
35.44/4

83 **Waistcoat,** 1780-90; cream plush, the back and lining
of cream twilled cotton except for the front and front
skirt, lined with cream twilled silk. The waistcoat is
double-breasted but collarless.
Condition: fair; soiled
34.246

84 **Waistcoat,** 1780-90; pink satin, quilted with vertical
lines of chain stitch, and with thick padding of un-
combed wool; pocket-flaps and surrounds, and narrow
borders, embroidered with chenille, spangles and ribbon
embroidery; the back is of rose-pink glazed wool; the
front edges and skirts are lined with cream twilled silk,
the rest of the lining is of a cotton and linen mixture.
Condition: good except for wear under arms
46.45/2   *Plate 18*

85 **Waistcoat,** 1780-90; silk waistcoat, with vertical white
satin stripes alternating with yellow stripes woven with
black spots; square-cut standing collar to be turned
back to form revers; the back is cream glazed twilled
wool, the lining fawn cotton.
Condition: good
48.108

86 **Waistcoat,** 1785-90; cotton woven with fine grey and white horizontal stripes and small pink and yellow flowers; sewn-on silk ribbon borders woven with green and yellow flowers; the back and lining are of white cotton. The bottom edge is now straight and the only remaining hint of a skirt is in the curving away of the front edges at the base.
Condition: good
54.78/5

87 **Waistcoat,** 1780-90; brown cloth, with standing collar and short skirt; the front and skirt edges are lined with cream twilled silk, the rest of the lining is of white cotton. The waistcoat is absolutely plain and possibly belonged to a suit.
Condition: poor
39.5/51

88 **Waistcoat,** 1785-90; cream corded silk embroidered in coloured silks with a pattern of thistles and con-volvulus, mostly in satin stitch; the lining of the front edges, also the back, are of white twilled silk. The standing collar, the short length and the disappearance of the skirt are all characteristic of the 1780s. The embroidery is of particularly high quality; the colours used, and the proportion of pattern to background, are reminiscent of the Chinese embroidery and painted fabrics sometimes found in women's dresses in the 1780s.
Condition: good; slightly spotted
A 15028

89 **Waistcoat,** 1785-90; cream satin, square shape with revers, elaborately embroidered at base, below slit pockets, with birds under a net in a flowered terrain; the rest of the area is embroidered with flowers between vertical white chenille stripes and with vandyked borders of applied blue satin covered with white net (knotted). There is a white fringe at the standing collar and front edges; the front and bottom edges are lined with cream satin, the rest of the lining and the back are of twilled cotton (possibly a replacement).
Condition: fairly good, soiled
Z 8005

90 **Waistcoat,** 1785-95; dull green silk, embroidered with flower border and sprigs in pink and green silks worked in chain stitch, with an applied embroidered blue silk medallion at the base each side, below the slit pockets; back and lining of linen. The waistcoat is the square-cut shape characteristic of the latter part of the century, though not yet as short as it was eventually to become.
Condition: good
C 1566

91 **Waistcoat,** 1785-95; pink corded silk woven with narrow horizontal silver stripes; no collar, fairly large pointed lapels; borders of white and silver ribbon with spangles; the back is of pink glazed wool; the front and front bottom edges are lined with cream twilled silk, the rest of the lining is a linen and cotton mixture.
Condition: good
34.167/4

92 **Waistcoat,** 1735-95; double-breasted waistcoat of horizontally-striped green and cream silk with woven black and white spots; fairly large pointed lapels, no collar, silver braid sewn on at the edges; the back is of green glazed twilled wool, the front and front bottom edges are lined with green twilled silk, the rest of the lining is a linen and cotton mixture.
Condition: good
34.167/7

93 **Waistcoat,** 1787-95; double-breasted waistcoat of pale greyish satin woven with flower border and all-over sprig in cream and brown; made with a narrow standing collar and wider lapels; the front and bottom front edges are lined with cream twilled silk, the back and lining is a white linen and cotton mixture. This material appears in a pattern book of Maze and Steer (from the Warner archive) now in the Victoria and Albert Museum (T.384-1972) dating from the winter of 1787.
Condition: good.
34.167/8   *Plate 20*

94 **Waistcoat,** 1785-95; satin, woven with cream trellis-pattern stripes alternating with mauve stripes with large shaded blue spots; the waistcoat is cut in the usual square shape with a narrow standing collar, and revers; the front lining and the back are of white linen and cotton mixture.
Condition: good
39.17

95 **Waistcoat,** 1785-95; cream satin waistcoat with meandering borders embroidered in coloured silks worked in chain stitch; the waistcoat is square-cut; the standing collar, now made to turn over to form revers, appears to have been subjected to some alteration; the back and lining are of white cotton.
Condition: good
40.1

96 Waistcoat, 1785-95; white checkered muslin over pink silk; narrow chintz borders with a twisted ribbon pattern picked out in gilt chain stitch; slit pocket each side worked with a similar border, tassels embroidered each side of the centre front from neck to waist in gold thread worked in chain stitch; there are spangles over the whole area; the waistcoat is collarless, with sharply-pointed revers; the back and lining are of white linen.
Condition: good except for some missing spangles
46.45/3

97 Waistcoat, 1785-95; double-breasted white cotton waistcoat with standing collar and revers; the borders and pockets are embroidered with stem and flower pattern in coloured wools worked in chain stitch; the back and lining are of white cotton.
Condition: soiled, the embroidery very worn
47.53/3

98 Waistcoat, 1785-95; similar to the last except that the embroidery is worked in stem and satin stitch. Both waistcoats appear to be home-made.
Condition: fair, slightly soiled
47.53/4

99 Waistcoat, 1785-95; cream twilled silk with vertical stripes of ribbon pattern embroidered in blue and silver and alternating with vertical strips of applied white ribbon edged with silver; the back and lining are of white cotton; the collar is made for turning back to form revers.
Condition: good
53.130/20

100 Waistcoat, 1785-95; pale green corded silk, embroidered in coloured silks with a pattern of fantastic vegetation, the back made of white linen; the front lining is white silk, the back lining white cotton; the waistcoat is made with a narrow standing collar and revers.
Condition: good
63.85/4

101 Waistcoat, unfinished, 1790-95; two rectangles of pale blue silk, embroidered in coloured silks and appliqué for waistcoat fronts, with leaf borders and sprigs and a panel at the base, below the slit pocket, of fantastic beasts; there is also an embroidered band for one of the slit pockets.
Condition: good though unfinished
A 9133-6

102 **Waistcoat,** 1790-95; double-breasted waistcoat of cream silk woven with a pink and yellow spot pattern; fairly wide shawl collar; the front and bottom edges are lined with cream twilled silk; the back and the rest of the lining are white cotton.
Condition: good
34.167/3

103 **Waistcoat,** 1790-1800; cream twilled silk, the back of cream twilled wool, lined with fawn cotton; the waistcoat has the characteristic square shape of the last decade of the century; it also has brass buttons with the Prince of Wales' crest and 'R.K.B.'.
Condition: good; slightly spotted
A 15035 (LM Cat 1935, p 139)

104 **Waistcoat,** 1790-1800; probably altered from an earlier waistcoat; silver tissue with a woven border and all-over sprig (similar to nos 57, 58, 67), made in the square shape of the end of the century but showing signs of alteration; the back is of white silk, the front lining of white silk, the back lining white linen.
Condition: fair, rather worn
A 21021

105 **Waistcoat,** 1790-1800; horizontally-striped yellow and grey watered silk; feather and ribbon border woven in brown; made with a standing collar and lapels; the back is of a linen and cotton mixture; the bottom front edges are lined with cream twilled silk, the rest of the lining is white cotton.
Condition: good
46.45/5

106 **Waistcoat fronts** (not made up), 1790-1800; a rectangle of white corded silk, embroidered for a pair of waistcoat fronts with applied spangled red ribbon borders, vertical stripes worked in purple and green silks and spangles; applied engraved medallions at base, with embroidered weeping willow trees and bowls of fruit.
Condition: good though unfinished
51.21   *Plate 21*

107 **Waistcoat fronts** (not made up), late-18th century; a pair of rectangles of white cotton with woven vertical stripes, flower borders, and buttons, embroidered in coloured silks.
Condition: stained
A 9137

108 **Waistcoat,** late-18th century; white silk woven with a silver thread; the front edges and slit pockets are worked with a border of embroidered flowers, and applied net (machine-made) over lozenges of terracotta silk; the rest of the area is embroidered with floral sprigs; the fronts are lined with white silk, the back is a single layer of white linen. The shape is the square one of the 1790s, the angular decoration indicates a date near 1800.
Condition: fair; the applied net very worn
A 12529

109 **Waistcoat,** late-18th century; white cotton, embroidered in white cotton with oak and acorn borders and all-over sprigs; the back, and the front lining, are of coarser white cotton. The waistcoat is the short type with a completely straight lower edge, characteristic of the last years of the 18th century.
Condition: good; stained
A 16483

Breeches

110 **Breeches,** 1760-80; white silk woven with flowers in trellises, in cut and uncut green and white velvet pile; the centre back waist fastens with a strap across the open top of the centre back seam; the front fastens with a falling flap lined with white satin; there are four buttons at the knee, and a band at the edge.
Condition: good, soiled
Z 8006

111 **Breeches,** 1770-90; brown silk, figured with a leaf pattern on a fine trellis ground, and lined with brown twilled wool; the centre back waist fastens with lacing over the open top of the centre back seam; the front fastens with a satin-lined front flap, and the knees with four buttons and straps.
Condition: fairly good
34.203

112 **Breeches,** 1770-90; turquoise silk, woven with a fine checker pattern in velvet pile; the centre back waist fastens with a strap over the open top of the centre back seam; the front fastens with a falling flap lined with white linen, the knees with four buttons and an embroidered kneeband fastening with a buckle.
Condition: fair; soiled
34.204

113 **Breeches,** 1780-90; narrow vertical stripes of black velvet pile on pale blue silk; the centre back waist fastens with a strap over the open top of the centre back seam, and the front with a falling flap, lined with white

linen; there are five embroidered buttons at the knee, and an embroidered kneeband fastening with steel buckles (one missing).
Condition: fair
Z 717

114 **Breeches,** 1780-90; fine undulating vertical stripes of black uncut velvet on a green silk ground; the centre back waist fastens with lacing over a gusset, the front with a falling flap lined with cream twilled silk; the knees fasten with three buttons and a strap with a gilt buckle (one missing).
Condition: fair
47.53/11

115 **Breeches,** 1780-95; black cloth; the centre back waist fastens with a buckled strap over a gusset, the front with a wide flap-fastening lined with black twilled silk; there are four buttons at the knee, and an embroidered kneeband fastening with steel buckles.
Condition: good, but the cloth has become greenish
Z 716

116 **Breeches,** 1780-1800; black twilled silk, the back waist fastening with lacing over a small gusset, the front with a falling flap lined with cream twilled silk; three buttons, and a strap with a gilt buckle (one missing) at the knees.
Condition: fair
39.5/41

117 **Breeches,** 1790-1800; black twilled silk; the centre back waist fastens with lacing over a central gusset, the front with a falling flap lined with black linen; there are four buttons and a band at the knee.
Condition: fragile
A 12986

118 **Breeches,** 1790-1800; black satin; the centre back waist fastens with lacing over a central gusset, the front with a falling flap lined with black twilled silk; there are four buttons at the knee, and a band fastening with a steel buckle. The sewing is of particularly high quality.
Condition: good
29.84/7

119 **Breeches,** late-18th century; yellow leather (buckskin); the centre back waist fastens with a buckle and strap over a centre gusset, and the front with a falling flap; there are six steel buttons at the knees, and a leather thong fastening; there is a little embroidery in blue cotton on the front flap and at the knee edge.
Condition: fairly good
39.5/57

Hats, Wigs and Wig-stands

120   **Wig-stand,** second half of the 18th century; hollow leather head-shape with front opening, on a turned wooden stand. Height $14\frac{1}{2}$ in.
Condition: good, base replaced
A 7357

121   **Wig-stand,** second half of the 18th century; similar to no. 120.
Condition: slightly worm-eaten. Height $15\frac{1}{2}$ in.
A 20979

122   **Wig,** 1780-1800; blonde horsehair wig, with side curls and pigtail.
Condition: fragile and soiled
A 15093

123   **Hat,** 1790-1800; black beaver, 'top-hat' shape with soft collapsible texture; narrow black ribbon band with buckle; lined with thin white silk and blue silk band.
Condition: rather battered
39.5/69

124   **Hat,** 1790-1800; light brown woollen cloth with a nap; fairly tall tapering crown, brown silk band with centre front bow; fairly narrow brim curling up slightly at sides; white silk lining.
Condition: good but the pile rather worn
53.170/1   *Plate 22*

125   **Hat,** 1790-1800; black plush; high tapering crown; wide black ribbon band with bow in front, brim curling up slightly at sides; lined with fawn twilled cotton.
Condition: fair; rather worn
54.63/1

Gloves

126   **Gloves,** second half of the 18th century; green silk, machine-knitted in stocking-stitch; spray pattern embroidered on back of hand in metal thread and spangles.
Condition: fairly good apart from a few holes
A 12546-7 (LM Cat 1935, p 176)

Footwear

127   **Shoes,** 1760-80; low-heeled, and fastening with ties over tongue at instep; made of blue satin, woven with silver thread and coloured silks in lozenge and flower pattern.
Condition: poor
A 15074 (LM Cat 1935, p 185)

128 Shoes, 1770-1800; flat-heeled, with pointed toes and ties fastening over the instep; made of cream corded silk embroidered with a floral pattern in metal thread and strip.
Condition: poor
A 12550-1

129 Shoe (one only), late-18th century; low-heeled white kid shoe, the heel covered with red leather, fastening with ties (missing) over tongue at instep; lined with pale blue silk.
Condition: fairly good
Z 8008

130 Boots, late-18th century; low-heeled square-toed calf-length boots of green leather, seamed over the instep, the front foot section a shade paler than the leg section.
Condition: good
51.74/3

Dressing-gowns

131 Dressing-gown, second half of the 18th century; this voluminous full-skirted garment would appear to be reversible, and to have been made of fabrics belonging to two different dates. The fawn brocaded silk on one side is the earlier, the blue glazed chintz on the other the later of the two.
Condition: the brocade very worn, the chintz good
53.101/10

132 Dressing-gown, 1770-80; long double-breasted dressing-gown, slightly shaped with a standing collar; the right front fastens over the left with ties, over single-breasted waistcoat fronts; the garment is made of chintz, quilted with a lozenge pattern worked in running stitch, and it is lined with cream linen.
Condition: good
58.40   *Plates 11, 12*

Shirt

133 Shirt, late 18th century; white linen, gathered at neck with top-stitched shoulder bands and gusset, and deep standing collar fastening with two worked buttons and buttonholes; the long sleeves are gathered into the shoulder and onto a narrow band at the wrist.
Condition: good
57.129/2

Acknowledgements

Thanks are due to all those who have helped in the
compilation of this catalogue; particularly, Miss Janet
Arnold for her invaluable help in dating the wig no 122; Miss
Anne M. Buck, lately Keeper of the Gallery of English
Costume, Platt Hall, Manchester; M. Robert de Micheaux of
the Musée des Tissus, Lyon; Miss Kay Staniland, Curator of
Costume, the London Museum and Miss Natalie Rothstein
and Miss Wendy Hefford of the Department of Textiles at
the Victoria and Albert Museum.

List of Sources

Gifts

Mrs E A Abbey 4, 9, 13, 26, 27, 28, 31, 35, 37, 39, 40, 41, 103, 116, 117, 119, 123
Miss B Andreae 77
Miss Blackett 109
Mrs Blandford 101, 107
Miss M E Cavan 133
Mrs Chamberlayne 91, 92, 93, 102
Miss A Cockerell 99
Mme Doreen Erroll 38, 69, 97, 98, 114
Miss M Gibson 50
Mrs Glanville 106
Miss J Haes 75
Miss Harcourt 22
T Heslewood 19
Miss L Hogarth 80
Mrs Hutchinson 94
J G Joicey 2, 5, 8, 10, 16, 18, 30, 32, 33, 36, 49, 58, 61, 62, 63, 64, 74, 104, 108, 122, 126, 127, 128
Miss S Mills 21, 79, 82
C A Minoprio 100
R Piper 11, 12, 20, 34, 118
Mrs D Rogers 68, 84, 96, 105
E C Russell 95
F H W Sheppard 85
H Strudwick 44, 56
Lady Thesiger 132
H Lyon Thompson 120
Miss H Trevelyan 76
Mrs Tupper 14

Loans

Lady Anson 130
Sir Guy Laking 57
Cecil F Beonell 90
Col C B Thackeray 54, 66, 67
The Right Hon the Lord Wharton 23, 55, 70

Purchases

Miss B Bennett 24, 43, 71, 73, 86, 121, 124, 125, 131
J S Lucas 1, 3, 6, 7, 17, 59

Anonymous Sources

15, 25, 29, 42, 45, 46, 47, 48, 51, 52, 53, 60, 65, 72, 78, 81, 83, 87, 88, 89, 110, 111, 112, 113, 115, 129

Bibliography

[Cruso, Thalassa]. London Museum Catalogues; No 5 Costume. (1935)

Cunnington, C. W. and **Cunnington, Phillis.** Handbook of English Costume in the 18th century. (Faber 1957)

Cunnington, Phillis and Lucas, Catherine. Occupational Costume in England from the 11th century to 1914. (Black 1967)

Davenport, Millia. The Book of Costume, II. (Crown Publishers, New York, 1948)

Kelly, F. M. and **Schwabe, R.** A Short History of Costume and Armour, 1066-1800. (Batsford 1931)

Leloir, M. Histoire du Costume, VIII IX X XI. (H Ernst 1933)

Thornton, P. Baroque and Rococo Silks. (Faber 1965)

Waugh, Norah. The Cut of Men's Clothes 1600-1900. (Faber 1964)

Printed in Scotland for Her Majesty's Stationery Office
by R. & R. Clark Ltd., Edinburgh
Dd 503884 K48 7/73